INTRODUCTION

They were oddballs, outsiders, misfits – passionate adventurers who took huge risks and pursued dangerous paths. They all suffered for their work – facing excommunication, becoming outcasts or even being hounded by an early version of the paparazzi. But their legacy was immense. Before they came along, humanity had for centuries been stumbling around in the dark. Then these individuals switched on the light and transformed our vision of the world for ever.

Six Experiments that Changed the World looks at the lives and work of six scientists:

- Galileo Galilei and the law of falling bodies

- Sir Isaac Newton and the nature of light

- Michael Faraday and electricity

- Gregor Mendel and the laws of heredity

- Marie Curie and radioactivity

- Albert Einstein and the theory of relativity

These five men and one woman had an unstoppable curiosity that led them to grapple with scientific problems that even the greatest minds of the day had been unable to solve. In illuminating these 'mysteries', they were often trying to come to terms with questions about their own lives. Sir Isaac Newton, for example – abandoned by his mother at the age of three – grew up an introverted semi-recluse, ruthlessly devoted to his studies to the exclusion of all else.

The experiments they conducted were all incredibly simple. In fact, in the Channel 4 series, the presenter Ken Campbell – who goes back in time to retrace the steps of these famous scientists – is able to recreate most of their experiments in his garden shed! Yet they often called for huge resources of time, patience and dedication. Marie Curie spent four years working to the point of exhaustion in primitive conditions in a makeshift laboratory, grinding, dissolving, filtering and crystallising huge quantities of tar-like material. Gregor Mendel studied more than 28,000 pea plants.

But the discoveries, when they came, were ground-breaking, seditious even. Galileo – by observing that the planets did not, in fact, orbit the Earth but the Sun – was challenging the reigning orthodoxy of the Catholic Church, and was forced to recant his 'heretical' views. He was put under house arrest in a villa near Florence, where he remained for the last nine years of his life.

Marie Curie suffered for her work, too. After discovering radium, she was hounded by the press, becoming one of the first paparazzi victims of the 20th century, and may have developed the disease that killed her as a result of her exposure to radioactive materials.

Yet without Curie, ironically, we would have no radiation therapy for treating cancer. Without Mendel, there would be none of the advances in genetic science. Without Faraday, our electricity-based lifestyles would be impossible.

And without Galileo? In 1971, during the Apollo 15 moon landing, the astronauts acknowledged their debt to him by dropping a hammer and feather on the moon. The objects fell exactly the way the maverick Italian scientist had predicted more than 300 years earlier.

Presenter Ken Campbell

GALILEO GALILEI
THE LAW OF FALLING BODIES

IT MAY BE HARD TO IMAGINE, but there was a time when priests rather than scientists decreed the laws of science. That was what Italy and other parts of the Western world were like when Galileo Galilei was born in Pisa in 1564.

Although the Renaissance was at its height, it had not led to a liberation in scientific thought. In fact, the Catholic Church – in its Counter Reformation against the rise of Protestantism – was doing everything it could to keep a grip on power. The Inquisition, the threat of excommunication and the very real risk of execution – the Church burned the philosopher Giordano Bruno at Rome in 1600 – helped put potential heretics in their place.

No matter how good your ideas, it was simply not possible to disagree publicly with the Church's view of nature, which was based on the theories of Aristotle (384–322 BC) and Ptolemy (2nd century AD). In astronomy, these held that the Earth sat at the centre of a perfect universe, with the heavenly bodies, including the Sun, circling round it – perfect spheres in the celestial dome. And Aristotle's physical laws were also holy writ.

So, when a young, outspoken Italian named Galileo Galilei began contradicting the Church's dogma with his experiments and observations, it was sure to cause a stir.

CHANDELIERS AND PENDULUMS
Galileo did not have an easy start in life. His father, Vincenzio Galilei, claimed to be of noble birth but was simply a musician who constantly argued with his patrons about the mathematics behind musical harmony and the rhythms of nature. Such arguments, while perhaps stimulating the young Galileo's mind, tended to reduce patronage, and the family was always short of money.

Following a monastic education, during which time his family moved to Florence, it was decided that Galileo should study medicine, Vincenzio hoping that his son might make a better life for himself as a doctor. In 1581, at the age of 17, Galileo entered Pisa University.

Top: The creation of life on Earth as seen by the Catholic Church – part of Michelangelo's Sistine Chapel ceiling of 1510. *Vatican Museums and Galleries/Bridgeman Art Library*

Above: Ptolemy's planetary system, with the Earth as the centre of the universe. *Mary Evans/Explorer*

Legend has it that, during his first year there, Galileo noticed a chandelier, suspended from the ceiling in the cathedral, swinging in the wind. By counting the timing of each swing using the beats of his pulse, he observed something that no one had realised before: the time it takes for a pendulum to swing to and fro is the same regardless of the length, or amplitude, of the swing – a property we now call isochronism. This discovery, although probably apocryphal in the detail, would lead to the development of accurate timekeeping, regulated with a pendulum.

BIRTH OF THE 'WRANGLER'

Galileo quickly grew bored with 16th-century medicine. The more he observed the world and listened to what he was being taught, the more he realised that something was sorely amiss with 'science'. Just as his father saw that rigid theory was stifling new musical forms, so Galileo, his eldest son, came to see the Aristotelian view as restraining scientific inquiry. But tact was not Galileo's forte. His fiery arguments, quick-witted retorts and quarrels with colleagues and professors led them to nickname him the 'wrangler'.

When Galileo ran out of money in 1585, he dropped out of university to follow his interest in mathematics and science. He returned to Florence, got a position as a lecturer at the Florentine Academy and began inventing in his spare time. His 1589 'theory of the centres of gravity of objects' won him the honourable, albeit poorly paid, post of mathematics lecturer at Pisa University. He remained there for three years and then, in 1592, moved on to a mathematics professorship at the University of Padua, where he flourished for 17 years.

It was during this period that he made a concerted attack on Aristotle's theories on motion that then prevailed in physics (*see box on page 4*).

FROM THE EARTH TO THE STARS

Galileo began to regard Aristotelian philosophy and Ptolemaic astronomy with increasing unease. In 1609, when he heard about a new device that could make distant objects appear closer, he reasoned it might help him study the heavens and so settle his mind. He improved on the original Dutch design of the telescope and began looking skywards.

He saw that the surface of the Moon was not smooth and perfect but full of craters, and realised the Milky Way was made up of countless stars, none of which was orbiting the Earth. He saw spots marring the surface of the Sun, and crucially observed moons orbiting Jupiter. This last discovery had a profound effect. If the Earth truly was at the centre of the universe with all the heavenly bodies circling it, as Ptolemy claimed, how could some of them be spinning around Jupiter?

Galileo rushed into print in 1610 with his book *The Starry Messenger*. The papal court was at first impressed, despite the fact that Galileo had contradicted Ptolemy and implied that the theory of the Earth orbiting the Sun – propounded by the Polish astronomer Copernicus in 1513 – was true. Galileo's popular lectures and fast-selling books soon created a groundswell of public opinion. He was offered a lifetime appointment to Padua University – much to the chagrin of the Aristotelian professors, who feared that his observations could lead to the crumbling of their philosophy and their livelihoods. Fortunately for them, Galileo refused the offer, took up the patronage of the Grand Duke of Tuscany and moved back to Florence.

For the Aristotelians, the only course of action was to raise suspicions about Galileo's motives in the eyes of the Church. After all, who was this upstart to tell the world that he could interpret God's universe better than the theologians?

The Jesuit cardinal Robert Bellarmine first tried to warn Galileo that his ideas would lead to trouble, and then, on 5 March 1616, issued a decree that declared Copernicus, and therefore Galileo, wrong. Galileo lay low for a while but continued his studies, developing new ideas and working on experiments to prove them.

TWO SYSTEMS ON A COLLISION COURSE

In 1623, Galileo dedicated his latest book on the nature of reality to the new pope Urban VIII who had been a good friend and protector to him in the past. Urban was rather pleased and Galileo went to Rome hoping to have the earlier decree revoked. Instead, the papal court granted him permission to write about his ideas as

This page
Above: Frontispiece of Galileo's *Dialogue Concerning the Two Chief World Systems*, depicting Aristotle (*left*), Ptolemy (*centre*) and – Galileo's hero – Copernicus. *Science Photo Library*

Background: The chandelier in Pisa Cathedral, said to have inspired Galileo's thinking about pendulums. *Mary Evans*

Page 5
Top: An 1882 rendition of Galileo's recanting of his belief in a Sun-centred universe. *Mary Evans*
Bottom: An Apollo 15 astronaut working on the Moon in 1971. *NASA/Science Photo Library*

BUCKETS, JARS AND BALLS

DURING HIS TIME at Pisa, Galileo allegedly dropped two cannon balls – one heavier than the other – from the top of the Leaning Tower. Aristotle had said that objects fall with a speed proportional to their weight. Thus the heavier ball should travel faster than the lighter one. Galileo hypothesised that the balls would both accelerate as they fell, but they should hit the ground at the same instant.

But this experiment, if it was ever carried out, was doomed to failure. Air resistance, which plays a key part in the study of falling objects, would have meant that the lighter ball would always fall more slowly. Galileo's experiment would also have happened so quickly that it would have been impossible to do accurate measurements.

It was another experiment, in around 1604, that proved Galileo's point. This involved some very simple apparatus but led to a fundamental law of engineering and mechanics.

Galileo thought that if he could slow the motion of the balls, he would not only reduce the effect of air resistance but would also be able to carry out accurate measurements. His solution? He used a slope, or inclined plane. He made a wooden ramp about 7 metres (23 feet) long and 30 centimetres (12 inches) wide. Along its entire length was a straight groove just a little wider than a finger's width, which was so well polished that a bronze ball could roll down it easily, with little friction.

Galileo also had to find a way to measure time accurately – not an easy task in an era when there were no accurate clocks. (In fact, it would be Galileo's own work on the pendulum that would lead to the development of modern clocks.) He made a hole in the bottom of a bucket and suspended a jar immediate-ly below the hole. He filled the bucket with water, blocking the hole with a finger. The moment he let a ball go down the ramp, he unblocked the hole and water flowed into the jar. When the ball hit a block at a set point on the ramp, he again blocked the hole. The bucket and jar were, in effect, a rudimentary stop-watch, and the water in the jar represented the time it took the ball to roll down the ramp.

Again and again, Galileo rolled the ball down the slope, measured (in water) the time it took to reach marked divisions on the slope and then compared the times. When he had collected enough data, he did a few calculations until he was able to work out a rule about the ball's motion. Scientists before Galileo had noted that objects accelerate as they fall – in other words, the longer something has been falling, the faster it drops. Galileo's achievement was to prove this through experiments and to calculate the distance–time relationship: the distance a falling body travels is directly proportional to the square of the time it has been in motion. Therefore, if it took one second for the ball to travel one unit of length, according to Galileo's rule it would take the ball four seconds to travel 16 units. Galileo also found that the weight of the ball did not matter – balls of different weights all arrived at the end of the ramp in the same time.

Although he had proved Aristotle wrong, Galileo was instructed by his academic masters to ignore his findings. He responded sarcastically, 'If experiments are performed thousands of times in all seasons and in every place without once producing the effect described by the philosophers, poets and historians, this means nothing and we must believe their words and not our own eyes.'

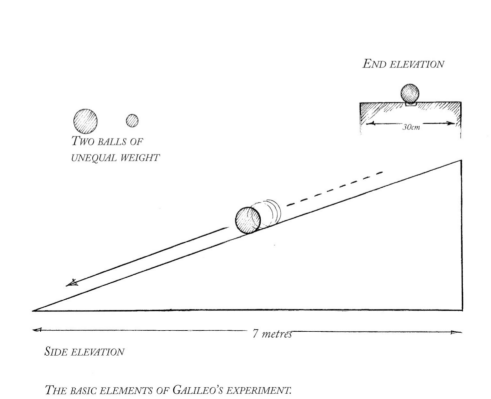

END ELEVATION

30cm

*TWO BALLS OF
UNEQUAL WEIGHT*

7 metres

SIDE ELEVATION

THE BASIC ELEMENTS OF GALILEO'S EXPERIMENT.

long as he presented a balanced perspective of both the Copernican heliocentric (Sun-centred) and the Ptolemaic geocentric (Earth-centred) systems.

The resulting book, *Dialogue Concerning the Two Chief World Systems – Ptolemaic and Copernican,* published in 1632, was strongly biased towards Copernican theory. The Church was furious and banned the book. Galileo was charged with heresy and, in April 1633, was taken to Rome for trial.

In a moment of unheard-of leniency, the Church offered Galileo a deal: if he recanted his belief that the Earth moves around the Sun, he would avoid life imprisonment and instead be placed under house arrest on his estate at Arcetri near Florence. Galileo agreed and publicly declared his theories null and void and put the Earth back as the static centre of the universe. However, legend has it that, as he left the court, Galileo stubbornly muttered: *'Eppur si muove'* – 'And yet it *does* move.'

Ensconced at Arcetri, Galileo continued to theorise and experiment on the nature of the universe, despite the fact that he had become blind. He died in 1642, still an exponent of the geocentric system in the eyes of the Church.

THE LEGACY

If his lack of diplomacy landed Galileo in trouble, his remarkable ability to reduce problems to very simple terms on the basis of everyday experience and common sense established his mind as one of the greatest in science. His fundamental concepts on motion were fleshed out by Isaac Newton (*see page 6*) in his laws of motion. But even more importantly, Galileo's use of experiment and observation to prove mathematical calculations on natural phenomena laid the foundations for the whole of modern science.

In 1971, the Apollo 15 astronauts dropped a hammer and a feather on the Moon. The two objects plummeted to the lunar surface, untroubled by air resistance, and

landed at precisely the same moment, proving Galileo correct 328 years after his death. The Catholic Church took a little longer. In 1979, Pope John Paul II set up a committee to study the Galileo case, and five years later its findings were made public. In 1992, the Vatican finally admitted that Galileo had been right.

(*see page 6*)

1564
Born at Pisa, Italy (15 February).

1581
Enters Pisa University to study medicine.

***c.* 1583**
Makes important discovery about the nature of pendulums.

1585
Drops out of medical school; begins investigating mathematics and physics.

1589
Publishes his ideas on the 'centre of gravity' of objects.

1592
Made professor of mathematics at Padua University.

***c.* 1604**
Carries out inclined plane experiment, which would lead to law of falling objects.

1610
Publishes The Starry Messenger. *Becomes philosopher and mathematician to Cosimo de' Medici II, the Grand Duke of Tuscany, who protects him from the Church.*

1616
Instructed by the Church to abandon the Copernican (heliocentric) theory.

1632
Publishes his scientific masterpiece, the Dialogue Concerning the Two Chief World Systems, *which destroys Aristotle and Ptolemy's world view.*

1633
Tried for heresy and placed under house arrest.

1638
Publishes Discourses and Mathematical Discoveries Concerning Two New Sciences.

1642
Dies at Arcetri, Italy (8 January).

SIR ISAAC NEWTON
THE NATURE OF LIGHT

of Fire-workes. 119
Sauciffons ; betwixt every of which, binde a knot of paper ſhavings, which will make it flye the better ; within a quarter of a yard of the cloth, let there bee bound a peece of prepared ſtoupell, the one end whereof, let touch the cloth, and the other, enter into the end of a Sauciffon:

A plate from John Bate's *The Mysteries of Nature and Art* – an early source of inspiration for Newton. *Science Museum/Science & Society Picture Library*

1642
Born at Woolsthorpe Manor, Lincolnshire (25 December)

1661
Enters Trinity College, Cambridge.

1664
Writes Certain Philosophical Questions, *containing his first observations about the divisibility of white light.*

1665
Black Death arrives at Cambridge. Newton forced to return home.

1667
Elected fellow of Trinity College.

c. 1668
Newton's experimentum crucis - proves white light is made up of colours.

ISAAC NEWTON, destined to become one of the most important scientists the world has ever known, was born on Christmas Day 1642 – the same year in which Galileo died and only three months after the beginning of the English Civil War. He did not have an auspicious start.

When he entered the world at Woolsthorpe Manor in Lincolnshire, Isaac Newton was so scrawny that it was said that he could fit inside a quart pot. He was not expected to live – but against the odds, he did.

When Isaac was just three (and the tide of the Civil War was turning in favour of the rebellious Roundheads), his mother Hannah left to marry a rector in a nearby town, his father – a poor yeoman farmer – having died before his birth. By all accounts, the separation from his mother scarred Newton for life. He certainly hated his stepfather and blamed his mother for abandoning him, while simultaneously feeling guilt, as if her leaving was because he had done something wrong. Freud would have had a field day.

Isaac was brought up by his maternal grandparents, the Ayscoughs, at Woolsthorpe. Unlike the Newtons – Isaac's father had died unable to write his own name – this side of the family was educated, and if young Isaac hadn't ended up with them, he might never have received any schooling. At the age of 12 – when Oliver Cromwell was securely in charge of the country as Lord Protector – he entered a grammar school in Grantham where he learned mostly Latin, Greek and Bible studies. He showed no early academic aptitude, but a fight with a bully, which he won, spurred him on to beat the other boy academically, too.

JUMPING IN THE WIND
Isaac, a solitary soul, also showed a remarkable practical ability, making kites, lanterns, and models driven by mice and rats. The inspiration for these mechanicals came from a book, *The Mysteries of Nature and Art* by John Bate, which he read at the age of 13. He also conducted simple experiments, such as trying to measure wind resistance by jumping into the wind.

In 1658, the same year that Cromwell died, 16-year-old Isaac's life was again turned upside down when his mother returned to Woolsthorpe – three children in tow – after the death of her second husband. She forced Isaac to leave school, and he had a miserable time unsuccessfully helping to run the family farm. He did not get on with his half-siblings and his relationship with his mother was uneasy.

Eventually she allowed him to go back to school, where he now excelled, and his supportive headmaster prepared him for university. In 1661, when he was 19, he went up to Trinity College, Cambridge. Remarkably for someone who was to apply mathematics to the physical forces of the universe, at this point Newton had received no mathematical training.

SCIENCE UNDER SCRUTINY
When Newton joined academia, Aristotle's elemental philosophy – based on the primacy of earth, air, fire and water – still largely held sway. Aristotle had also argued that light objects fall more slowly to earth than heavy ones and that nothing moved unless pushed or pulled by another force. However, after almost 2,000 years, these ideas were finally coming under scrutiny.

Through his experiments which involved rolling balls down slopes, Galileo (*see page 4*) had proved that moving bodies continue to move unless stopped by a force – that is, they have inertia. His use of the telescope had also given greater weight to Copernicus' hypothesis that the solar system was heliocentric (centred on the Sun). Meanwhile, the German astronomer Johannes Kepler had discovered that the orbits of planets were, in fact, elliptical, not circular, as had been assumed, and that the Moon affected the tides.

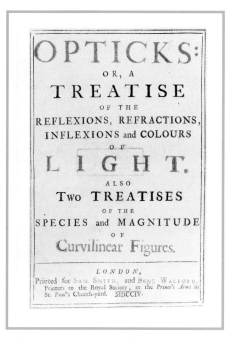

Left: Title page of Newton's *Opticks* of 1704. *Royal Society*

NEWTONIAN ANALYSIS
Chris Woods

His mother left and took his world away.
He felt empty and dark like deep space,
until stars and planets filled him up.
He could predict their complex movements,
trust them to be there.

The moon released tides of passion,
whirled round his mind,
dizzied him with desire.
He invented a telescope to bring her close,
stayed with her at night,

Such strange alchemy:
To his peers, he became precious metal,
brilliant but cold.
And like the firmament,
he appeared too remote.
Some worshipped him. None came near.

Now stars gather in the bowl of his telescope.
He lifts them to his eyes and drinks
in silent communion with himself.

From *Recovery*, Enitharmon Press, 1993

As Newton arrived at Trinity College, the accepted Aristotelian views of the world were being challenged by proponents of the 'inductive' scientific method advocated by Francis Bacon (1561–1626), in which general causes and conclusions are arrived at only after an exhaustive collection and processing of data. They were joined by supporters of the philosophy of René Descartes (1596–1650), which centred on the belief in a mechanistic, deterministic universe and the separation of body and spirit.

FREEDOM TO BE CURIOUS
Newton had grown into a difficult, introverted, reclusive young man who was at times argumentative and spiteful, but always ruthlessly devoted to his studies to the exclusion of all else. He also became renowned for his egotism and arrogance. Some accounts have him dabbling in the occult and black arts, inflicting injury on himself, suffering neuroses and near mental breakdown. To what extent these peculiarities of character contributed to his genius is a constant cause of scholarly debate.

When the Black Death arrived at Cambridge in 1665, the university closed for 18 months and Newton was forced to return home. This short period – which gave him the freedom to indulge his curiosity – proved to be the most astonishingly fruitful of his life. He devoured books on geometry and mathematics, soon mastering them and devising calculus – the mathematics of the rate of change. He also set to thinking about gravity, the nature of motion, what strength of force held the Moon in its orbit – and what a beam of white light actually is.

The year Newton returned home was the same year that scientist Robert Hooke (1635–1703) – whom Newton would come to regard as his arch-rival – published *Micrographia*, containing his theory about the nature of light, the study of which is scientifically known as 'optics'. Hooke believed that colours were caused by varying mixtures of light and darkness. Newton's own observations led him to doubt this, and his experiments with light (*see box on page 8*) would lead to one of his greatest discoveries.

CRITICISM AND FEUDS
Newton's brilliance saw him elevated through the ranks at Trinity. He was elected a fellow in 1667, then a professor of mathematics two years later, when he was only 26. However, his lectures were so difficult to comprehend that all the undergraduates walked out, leaving Newton reciting to the walls alone.

It wasn't until 1671 that the scientific community began to learn about his theories. Newton was persuaded to exhibit to the Royal Society a 'reflecting' telescope that he had designed and made himself. Using a mirror to focus light coming into the instrument, this achieved a magnification 40 times that of the best 'refracting' telescope, which used lenses and was much bulkier. Newton's first attempt, only 15cm (6in) long, is the direct predecessor of today's huge astronomical reflecting telescopes.

The year after his telescope demonstration, when Newton was invited to become

---

1669
Invents 'reflecting' telescope; becomes a professor of mathematics at Trinity and returns to subject of optics.

1672
Elected fellow of the Royal Society.

1676
Royal Society finds Newton's prism experiments bear out his hypothesis.

1684
Writes On Motion.

1687
Principia Mathematica *published.*

1696
Becomes warden of the London Mint, Bank of England (made master two years later).

1703
Elected president of the Royal Society.

1704
Publishes Opticks.

1705
Receives knighthood from Queen Anne.

1707
Publishes Arithmetica Universalis.

1727
Dies (20 March), aged 85, and is buried in Westminster Abbey, following a state funeral.

THE 'CRUCIAL EXPERIMENT'

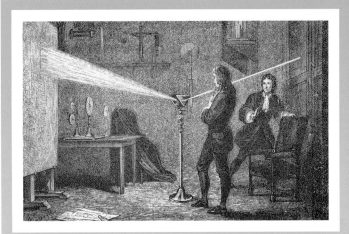

Newton using a prism to create a spectrum of colours from a beam of white light. *Mary Evans*

BY THE 1660s, it was well known that light shone through a prism produced a spectrum of colours – blues and purples at one end, red/orange at the other. However, it was commonly believed that light itself was indivisible – that, in fact, it was the prism itself that must be causing the colours. Newton wasn't so sure. He was so dedicated to the pursuit of truth that he risked blinding himself by sticking a bodkin – a blunt, thick needle – in his eye to alter the shape of the eyeball. Experiments such as this convinced him that current light theory was wrong.

Legend has it that, while wandering through Stourbridge market, Newton bought a prism and decided to experiment. In 1664, he made a spectrum by shining light through the lump of

glass and isolated the individual colours, observing that each one was refracted – 'bent' – to a different angle.

In 1669 and 1670, Newton returned to light experiments to prove his theory once and for all. This time he drilled a hole in a window shutter to create a narrow beam of light. He placed a prism in front of this beam and directed the light emerging from it on to a piece of card, which produced a spectrum of colours. The card had an even tinier hole in it, enabling Newton to isolate one of the colours – red – and direct it through another prism.

According to the accepted theory, the second prism should have changed the red light into something else. It didn't. Newton tried the same experiment with the blue light and achieved the same result. He concluded that the white light was made up of pure constituents of individual colours, each refracted to a different degree.

This experiment, which Newton called his *experimentum crucis*, would have been enough to prove his theory concerning the divisibility of light. But he went a step further, refocusing the spectrum through a lens to re-create white light at the focal point. He also invented a special cogged wheel, which he put between a lens and a focal point on the wall. When the wheel was turned, it blocked one of the constituents of white light thereby turning the light focused on the wall into the remaining colours of the spectrum.

These beautifully simple and logical experiments proved beyond doubt that light was not pure, but made up of the colours of the rainbow. Extraordinarily, Newton told no one about his work, and even when news of it did leak out, he refused to have it published, waiting until 1704 – the year after the death of his arch-rival Robert Hooke – to publish his book *Opticks*.

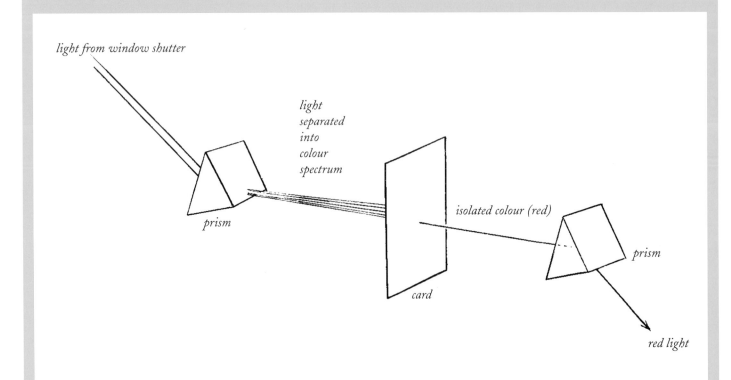

light from window shutter

light separated into colour spectrum

prism

isolated colour (red)

card

prism

red light

a fellow of the Royal Society, he felt bold enough to convey his theories about light to the other members. This embroiled him in a bitter and lifelong dispute with Robert Hooke, who claimed credit for much of Newton's work.

Newton hated criticism of any kind and loathed having to justify himself to people he felt were inferior. He had other feuds, notably with Sir John Flamsteed, the Astronomer Royal, and Gottfried Leibniz, the German philosopher. As criticism came from other quarters, he could take no more – and turned his back on the scientific community for over a decade.

THE LEGACY

Newton's withdrawal gave him the space to make even greater scientific discoveries, and some historians believe that this work paved the way for the Industrial Revolution. His thinking on gravity and the use of mathematics to explain the physical laws of the universe, enshrined in the *Principia Mathematica* (1687), would frame scientific thought for the next 200 years. Newton also found that the force that kept the planets revolving round the Sun – gravity – was the same that made an apple fall from a tree to the ground.

Newton's *Principia* contained his famous laws of motion, which were used to predict the existence of undiscovered planets. Even today, when space rockets are programmed to go to Saturn or Jupiter, scientists use these laws. We can predict the movement of the tides, the occurrence of eclipses, the stress encountered by a spinning washing machine, all by using Newton's laws.

Most significantly, Newton changed our view of the world to one in which physical phenomena are not arbitrary events but are governed by laws. The ancient Greek philosopher Pythagoras had suspected that mathematics was behind all harmony in the universe. Newton devised the mathematical formulae that made sense of these harmonies, these constant laws of physics.

Newton lived in an age of alchemy, magic and superstition and has gone down in history as the first of the rationalists, the first true scientist, who replaced sorcery with mathematics. But he was also a devoted alchemist, as fascinated by the possibility of transmuting base metals into gold as he was by the laws of physics – a difficult man of contradictions until his dying day.

Above: Isaac Newton: a portrait from a trade card issued by a chocolate manufacturer. *Mary Evans*

Below: Newton's 'gravity map'. A projectile is launched horizontally from a 'very tall mountain' (V). At low velocities, it travels short distances (D, E, F, G) before gravity forces it to strike the Earth. At high velocities (A, B), it escapes gravity to orbit the Earth. *Royal Observatory, Edinburgh/Science Photo Library*

Below left: Copy of the first reflecting telescope, built by Newton in 1721. *Science Museum/Science & Society Picture Library*

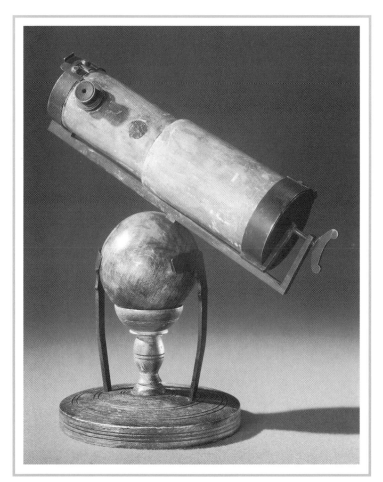

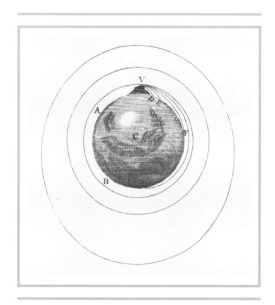

MICHAEL FARADAY
ELECTRICITY

AT THE BEGINNING of the 19th century, Newton's laws of physics were still intact and his view of the universe as a clockwork mechanism was helping to oil the wheels of the Industrial Revolution. The likes of English scientist Humphry Davy and the Frenchman Antoine Lavoisier were laying the foundations of modern chemistry. But there was one natural phenomenon that remained something of a mystery – electricity.

Scientists had, of course, studied lightning, they knew of electric eels, they could produce static electricity and, in 1786, Italian anatomist Luigi Galvani made a frog's legs kick by touching them with two different metals. The invention of the electric battery in about 1800 by Italian physicist Alessandro Volta had even given scientists one means of studying this elusive force.

The best theory at the time was that electricity was perhaps a fluid that flowed through wires like water through a pipe. Why then did a wire carrying a current make the needle of a compass spin? And if electricity was a fluid, why did it not pour out of the ends of the wires when they were disconnected?

The man who would shed light on the nature of electricity was Michael Faraday.

TO THE GREATER GLORY OF GOD

Faraday was born on 22 September 1791 in what was then the Surrey village of Newington Butts, now the Elephant & Castle area of south London. His blacksmith father had been forced out of Yorkshire earlier that year by the Industrial Revolution, which was swiftly eliminating traditional trades. Repeatedly ill, he rarely worked and his four children often had very little to eat.

The Faradays were devout members of the Sandemanians, an obscure Puritan sect who believed the Bible should be interpreted literally. Michael Faraday's religious faith was perhaps the single most important influence on his life. He held that nature had been created according to God's plan, and he saw his life's mission as understanding and explaining that plan in scientific terms to the greater glory of God.

Faraday received only a rudimentary education, although he did learn to read and write at Sunday school. He took an early job delivering newspapers and at 14 began an apprenticeship in the bookbinding trade. Unlike his workmates, he read many of the books he worked on, but it was the entry for 'electricity' in the *Encyclopaedia Britannica* that sparked his interest in science.

NOTE-TAKER AND BOTTLE-WASHER

Faraday managed to build himself a simple electrostatic generator from spare pieces of wood and bottles and performed various simple experiments. But his greatest inspiration came on 12 November 1812 when he was 21. He obtained a ticket to attend a lecture on chemical philosophy given by Sir Humphry Davy at the Royal Institution – a 'theatre of science', where experiments were carried out in front of a paying audience. Davy was a charismatic scientist with many female admirers, and subscriptions to his lectures funded a great deal of his research. The writer Mary Shelley may even have modelled her Dr Frankenstein on Davy.

Fascinated by Davy's lecture, Faraday took copious notes which he then wrote up, illustrated, indexed and lovingly bound to send to Davy as a tribute – together with a letter asking for employment in his laboratories. Davy refused, perhaps because he saw bookbinding as a better trade for a young working-class man. But Faraday persisted, and when Davy had to sack his assistant for brawling, Faraday was given the job of laboratory assistant, which at first amounted to no more than note-taker and bottle-washer.

Faraday, although largely self-taught, soon began to prove himself in Davy's lab, and in 1813 even went as secretary with Davy and his wife on a grand two-year tour

Above: Humphry Davy testing the miners' safety lamp that he designed in 1815. *Mary Evans*
Below: An illustration from a 19th-century science book showing Galvani's experiment, when he made a frog's legs kick by creating an electrical circuit between two different metals. *Mary Evans*

Fig. 405.

of France and Italy, visiting the leading scientists of the day, including Alessandro Volta. Faraday, having none of the preconceptions of others in the world of science, asked seemingly naïve questions of these eminent men. He simply wanted to know how things worked.

THE DANGLING WIRE

In 1820, Danish scientist Hans Christian Ørsted had theorised about why a compass needle would spin when exposed to a wire carrying an electric current. He reasoned that the wire might somehow be surrounded by magnetism, which then could interfere with objects close by. Shortly after Ørsted announced this, the French scientist André-Marie Ampère demonstrated that two parallel wires carrying an electric current in the same direction are attracted to each other, whereas when the currents flow in opposite directions, the wires are repelled. He also showed that a coil of wire behaves like a magnet when current flows through it.

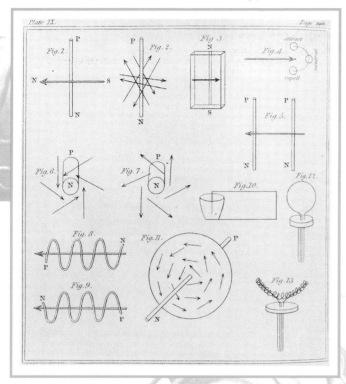

The editor of the *Philosophical Magazine* asked Faraday to investigate 'electromagnetism' – the ability of an electric current to produce magnetism – hoping that he could find out the truth behind all the wild theories and opinions that had resulted from Ørsted's theory. So at the age of 28, Faraday began to look into the problem with the simple purpose of understanding what was happening. He did not resort to complex mathematical equations like other scientists, but just carried out simple experiments and observed.

In 1821, the year in which he married Sarah Barnard, he completed a survey of all that was known of electricity and magnetism. He then decided to build a device to look more closely at what appeared to be a circular force surrounding wires carrying electricity. He dangled a copper wire into a bowl of mercury (a liquid metal that can conduct electricity) that contained a magnet at its centre. One end of a wire was placed in the mercury, with its other end attached to one terminal of a battery. An electric circuit was created by attaching (by wire) the metal stand from which the first wire was dangling to the other battery terminal.

Faraday reasoned that if there really was a circular force around wires carrying electricity, the dangling wire would be pushed away from the magnet. The results of Faraday's experiment proved what he had suspected: the dangling wire moved round and round in the mercury, indicating a circular force. In his notes, Faraday laconically described the result as 'Very satisfactory'. In reality he had created the world's first electric motor. But he did not stop there. He pondered the reverse effect of his experiment – he had generated a magnetic field from an electric current, but what about a magnetic field that generated a current of electricity? Faraday was about to tackle this (*see box on page 12*).

(*see box on page 12*)

Below left: Diagrams contained in Faraday's article on electricity and magnetism in the *Philosophical Magazine* in 1821. *Royal Society*

1791
Born Newington Butts, Surrey (22 September).

1812
Begins working for Sir Humphry Davy.

1820
Completes apprenticeship with Davy. Produces first carbon-chlorine compounds: C_2Cl_{16} and C_2Cl_{14}.

1821
Marries Sarah Barnard, settles permanently at the Royal Institution and begins experiments in electricity and magnetism.

1824
Elected fellow of the Royal Society.

1825
Discovers benzene.

1831
Begins working with Charles Wheatstone on the theory of sound. Carries out experiment that demonstrates electric induction.

1839
Produces theory of electrical action, bringing together his ideas and experiments. Suffers a physical breakdown.

1845
Returns to active research after protracted illness. Produces glass with very high refractive index, which leads to discovery of diamagnetism.

1855
Illness and senility begin to set in.

1867
Dies (25 August).

ELECTRICITY AND THE IRON RING

FOR 10 YEARS, scientists had been working on the problem of creating electricity from a magnetic field. They assumed that if they could make the magnet strong enough, they might be able to induce a current in a wire – but they all failed.

Faraday, meanwhile, was working with Charles Wheatstone (a scientist who had invented the concertina) on the theory of sound. Sound is basically the result of something vibrating at a frequency we can hear. It had been spotted that, when a violin bow was drawn across an iron plate that had been brushed with a light powder, wave-like patterns formed in the powder. Faraday suspected that the production of these vibration patterns was somehow related to the patterns that iron filings formed around a magnet and an electric wire.

The revelation came when Faraday and Wheatstone observed 'acoustic induction'. By drawing a bow across one powder-covered iron plate that had been placed close to a second, they noticed that the same vibration patterns could be produced on the second. Faraday reasoned that he might be able to induce a current in a wire in a similar manner.

On 29 August 1831, he took an iron ring – 2cm ($^7/_8$ in) thick and 15cm (6 in) in diameter – and wound one side with several layers of wire 'insulated' with twine and calico; when he connected this coil to a battery, it would become a magnet. He wound the opposite side of the ring with layers of uninsulated wire and connected that to a galvanometer, an instrument that detects and measures weak electric currents.

Faraday thought that, when the electromagnet was switched on, a 'wave' would be produced in the coil on the opposite side of the ring, which would show up as a movement of the galvanometer needle. As he connected the insulated coil to the battery, he saw the needle on the galvanometer flicker and return to 0. He had induced a current in the uninsulated coil in

Faraday's iron ring. *Adam Hart-Davis/Science Photo Library*

much the same way that the vibrations from the first iron plate had caused the second to resonate. Amazingly, when he switched off the electromagnet, the galvanometer twitched again, this time in the opposite direction. The receding 'wave' had also induced a current.

This was perhaps Faraday's most significant experiment. It demonstrated 'electric induction' - the process by which electrical properties are transferred, without physical contact, from one body to another. This lies at the heart of two processes vital to our lives today: electricity generation and the movement of an electric motor. Faraday went on to discover that, by moving a magnet in and out of a coil of wire, a current could be induced in the coil – an achievement that had eluded scientists for a decade.

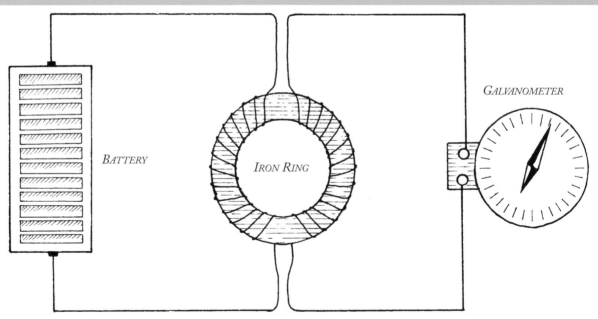

(a) First circuit wound around iron ring and connected to battery.

(b) Second circuit wound around iron ring and connected to galvanometer.

(c) Battery supplies power to coil on the left side of the iron ring, which induces a current in the separate coil on the right side, thereby registering a reading on the galvanometer.

BREAKDOWN

By 1839, Faraday had amassed countless experimental results and devised an encompassing theory to explain them – the general theory of electrical action. According to this, electricity – whose actual nature still remained a mystery – caused tensions to be created in matter. If these tensions were released, a wave of force – an electric current – would pass along the substance.

While Faraday is particularly famed as a physicist, his contributions to chemistry were just as important. He wrote a manual of practical chemistry, discovered a number of new compounds – including benzene from condensed oil gas – and was the first person to liquefy a gas. He also discovered the relationship between electricity and chemical bonding. But it was his crucial work on electricity and magnetism that laid the foundations for a whole century of discovery and invention.

Faraday now had as many if not more admirers as Davy had had in his heyday and was recognised as a 'great man of science'. However, he remained true to science and to his religion and did not patent a single invention, saying that his only motive in making these discoveries was to 'know the mind of God'. But all the work he had carried out finally took its toll: in 1839, he suffered a breakdown from which he never fully recovered, although he was able to return to research six years later.

UNIFIED FORCES

In 1846, Faraday gave a lecture, 'Thoughts on Ray Vibrations', at the Royal Institution. The ideas contained in it would help James Clerk Maxwell (1831–79) unite electricity and magnetism to form his electromagnetic theory of light. By 1850, Faraday had introduced the concepts of 'space' and 'force' that would eventually crack Newton's mechanistic vision of a clockwork universe. Space, he said, was not 'nothing' but a medium of particles surrounded by energy, which supports the strains created by electric and magnetic forces.

Faraday believed that all the forces are just manifestations of a single force. This 'unified theory of forces' is something physicists are still studying today. James Clerk Maxwell united electricity and magnetism in the 19th century. Electromagnetic and weak nuclear forces were united by Sheldon Glashow, Abdus Salam and Steven Weinberg in the late 1960s. However, the force of gravity stubbornly resists unification, despite the best efforts of Faraday and his successors, including Einstein.

Despite the esoteric areas into which his thinking occasionally drifted, Faraday was a great believer in popularising science, especially among children. He initiated Friday evening discourses for the public at the Royal Institution, and Christmas lectures for children – the most famous of which, 'The Chemical History of a Candle', was first given in 1860. The lectures continue to this day.

Yet Faraday remained a modest man and turned down both a knighthood and the presidency of the Royal Society; characteristically, he refused to take part in the preparation of poison gas for use during the Crimean War. In his last years, he was plagued by illness and senility, perhaps the result of frequent exposure to low levels of poisoning during his chemical research. He retired to an apartment at Hampton Court provided by Queen Victoria, where he died in 1867 at the age of 76. Perhaps as befits his roots – but not his accomplishments – the only public memorial to him is a small plaque under a flyover at the Elephant & Castle. However, he did receive a far more widespread fame: until recently his face appeared on the back of the £20 note.

Above: Michael Faraday. *Science Photo Library*
Below: Faraday lecturing to children. *Mary Evans*

GREGOR MENDEL
THE LAWS OF HEREDITY

1822

Born Johann Mendel at Heinzendorf, Austria (22 July).

1843

Becomes a monk at Brünn in Moravia, taking the name 'Gregor'.

1847

Ordained as a priest.

1851

Enters University of Vienna to study natural sciences.

1854

Returns to Brünn to teach at the technical high school.

1856

Begins experimenting with plant characteristics.

1865

Reports experimental results to the Brünn Society for the Study of Natural Science.

1866

Results published as Versuche über Pflanzen Hybride *(Treatises on Plant Hybrids).*

1868

Elected abbot of his monastery.

1884

Dies at Brünn (6 January).

1900

Mendel's laws independently unearthed.

SCIENTIFIC DISCOVERIES were coming thick and fast at the time of Mendel's birth in 1822. Steam power was already turning wheels, electricity was on the verge of being harnessed and chemistry was finally laying to rest the alchemists. But these innovations scarcely touched the life of the young Johann Mendel, the son of an Austrian peasant farmer.

Yet the discoveries made by the adult Mendel as he tended his monastery's kitchen garden would lead to a revolution in our understanding of life, and would ultimately give us, almost a century and a half later, a new industry – biotechnology.

THE BACKWATER OF BIOLOGY

While scientists were laying down the modern principles of physics and chemistry in the first half of the 19th century, biology remained very much a backwater. Animals and plants were considered as just specimens to count, kill and catalogue. Vast numbers of animals were collected from all over the world, to be exhibited in zoos or stuffed and placed in the thriving museums of natural history. The inner workings of organisms remained a mystery, and the best that scientists could do was to dissect and name the body parts and provide names and classes for different species.

Even the basics of reproduction were poorly understood. Fertilisation of an egg by a sperm was a vague concept, with some theories suggesting that the sperm carried all the information needed to create offspring, and others that there was a tiny person – a 'homunculus' – waiting to be born inside either the sperm or the egg.

Plant science was in a similar state. Horticulturists scoured the world for interesting new species, which they enthusiastically tore out by the roots to grow in their botanical gardens and hothouses. There was little thought about how variations arose in shape, size and patterns within a species.

A PREFERENCE FOR PEAS

Because his father was a farmer, it is perhaps not surprising that, from an early age, Johann Mendel was interested in the natural world of the family farm in Heinzendorf, then in Austria but now in the Czech Republic. Although he was a sickly and nervous boy, he was also bright and ambitious. He studied at the Philosophical Institute at

Above right: The Zoological Gallery in the British Museum, c. 1840. *Mary Evans*

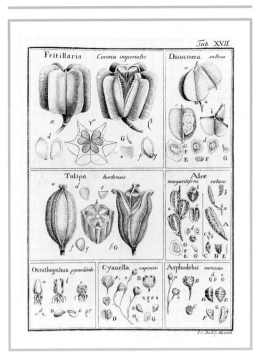

Olmütz for two years before entering – in 1843 at the age of 21 – the Augustinian monastery at Brünn, Moravia, taking the name 'Gregor'. He was perhaps attracted to the monastery because of its renown as a centre of learning and scientific endeavour. Its library contained plenty of scientific books, including ones covering agriculture, horticulture and botany, all of which Mendel devoured.

He was ordained as a priest in 1847, and two years later he worked briefly as a supply teacher of Greek and mathematics at a local secondary school. However, in 1850 he failed the examination to obtain a teaching licence – ironically, because of poor marks in biology and geology. The following year, his abbot sent him to the University of Vienna where he studied physics, chemistry, mathematics, zoology and botany. He returned to Brünn in 1854 to teach natural sciences at the technical high school, continuing this task for the next 14 years. During this time, he again failed to gain a teaching certificate.

On his return to the monastery, Mendel had taken charge of the kitchen garden. Now, with the tools of scientific reasoning that he had acquired at university, he began to experiment with the plants he grew. One particularly interesting crop was the edible pea – *Pisum sativa* (*see box on page 15*). Allegedly, many of his experiments were done simply for the fun of it. But he also spent time with scientifically aware colleagues at the high school and played an active part in the meetings of the Brünn Society for the Study of Natural Science.

A SCIENTIST AHEAD OF HIS TIME
Early in 1865, Mendel presented his studies on what he called 'plant hybridisation' to the Brünn Society for the Study of Natural Science, confidently stating that no one had studied or understood the basis of heredity in such a mathematical way before. Given the complexity of his results, he should probably have foreseen the response.

The newspapers described the audience as polite, but blankly uncomprehending – and these were mostly learned men. Mendel's mathematical approach to biology was just too far ahead of its time. It would not be until the late 20th century that the power of the computer would wield the full force of mathematics over heredity in the form of 'bioinformatics'.

It must have been terribly disappointing for Mendel when he presented the results of some eight years of pea breeding only to be met with blank incomprehension. In 1866, he published his results as *Treatises on Plant Hybrids*, with no more success than his Brünn presentation. However, despite this lack of recognition, he continued working and published one further paper in 1869 on hawkweed.

It is tempting to link Mendel's work to that of his contemporary Charles Darwin, who was developing his theory of natural selection. Darwin initially considered heredity to be a result of 'blending', in which characteristics from each parent are combined and transmitted through fluids in the blood. In the past, there was a

Above left: Mendel's garden at the Brünn monastery. A memorial to him is on the left. *Science Photo Library*
Above: The dissection of various seed pods: an illustration by Gaertner. *Royal Society*
Below: Illustration of an aloe plant by Ehret. *Royal Society*

PEAS AND GENES

IN 1856, Mendel began studying the characteristics of his pea plants. He monitored tallness and dwarfism, blossom colour, position of the flowers on the stem, leaf types, differences in seed colour and shape, and variations in the appearance of the pods. What he observed when he crossed peas with different combinations of these characteristics would lead him to the laws of heredity, which help explain how parents pass on their characteristics to their offspring.

Mendel's experiments each involved three stages.

1 Mendel exploited the fact that pea plants have both male and female sex organs. He divided his plants into groups with dif-fering characteristics, such as tallness and dwarfism, and self-pollinated the plants for several generations to produce dif-ferent groups, each exhibiting a 'pure' characteristic. This gave him generation P.

2 He cross-pollinated two of these groups – for example, one group with pink blossoms with one group with yellow blossoms. The offspring were called the first filial – or F1 – generation.

3 He then self-pollinated the F1 generation plants to produce the F2 generation and counted how many of the resulting F2 offspring had one or the other of the parental characteristics.

After he had done this experiment hundreds of times with thousands of plants, he began to see a pattern emerge in the characteristics of successive generations. The F1 generation always had offspring with only one parental characteristic. However, the F2 generation contained both parental traits.

The characteristic seen in every plant in the F1 generation he called 'dominant'. This was also the most common trait in the F2 generation, and Mendel observed that it occurred at the ratio of three to one. If tallness was dominant over dwarfism in the F1 generation, there would be three tall plants to one dwarf in the F2 generation. The trait that was not seen in F1 but appeared at a ratio of one to three in F2 was the 'recessive' trait.

Through repeated observations of more than 28,000 pea plants, Mendel deduced two major scientific laws. First, he reasoned that, for this pattern of traits to emerge, parents must carry pairs (one 'dominant' and one 'recessive') of heredity 'particles', and that each parent must pass on one of its pair to its offspring through its sex cells: an egg or sperm. This he called the *law of segregation*.

His second deduction was based on the observation that, when several pairs of opposing characteristics are seen in the peas, the pairs of heredity 'particles' produce all possible combinations in the offspring. They do this randomly, so that a short pea with wrinkly pods and purple blossoms was just as likely as a tall, white-blossomed plant with smooth pods – the *law of independent assortment*.

While Mendel knew nothing of the molecular basis for his laws, they helped him hybridise his pea plants to produce crops with specific characteristics. Indeed, the laws rely only on the assumption that there is a unit of heredity passed on to offspring via sexual reproduction. The nature of the units, which we now know as genes, was irrelevant to Mendel's laws.

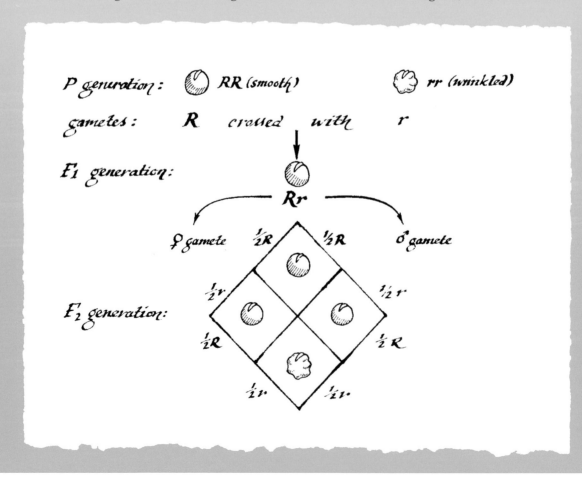

suspicion that Mendel's true motive was to demonstrate that 'blending' was not how heredity worked, so that he could discredit Darwin's work and show that humans had not descended from the apes but were created in God's image.

The only problem with this is that Mendel began working on his ideas before 1859, when Darwin went public with his own theory that would define heredity as the engine of evolutionary change. Ironically, Mendel's ideas actually cast suspicion on himself in the eyes of the Church.

Despite this, in 1868, he was elected abbot of his monastery and became a well-loved figure in Brünn. Administrative duties and political machinations with the Austrian government over the monastery's tax bill seem to have wasted much of his research time from then on. Yet he maintained an interest and worked in botany, bee culture and even meteorology almost to the time of his death in 1884, when he was 62.

REDISCOVERY

Mendel's discoveries lay dormant for decades until 1900, when three botanists – Carl Erich Correns in Germany, Hugo de Vries in the Netherlands and Erich von Tschermak-Seysenegg in Austria – independently developed theories to explain inherited characteristics. A cursory search of scientific literature revealed to them that the fundamentals had actually been discovered by a monk 34 years earlier. Mendel suddenly achieved posthumous fame. Scientists of the 20th century then took his theories further by describing the true nature of his heredity 'particles' – the chromosomes and genes.

Mendel's laws turned out not to be universal. While they work well for simple characteristics such as flower position and height in peas, there are numerous characteristics in plants and animals that are the product of more than one gene. In these cases, predicting certain characteristics in offspring becomes almost impossible.

In the 1930s, scientific controversy raged as to whether Mendel had falsified some of his data to make them fit his theories. British mathematician R A Fisher claimed that Mendel's statistical analysis of his figures did not fit Fisher's own statistical models. However, in 1968, the Austrian-Swedish genetic scientist H Lamprecht demonstrated that Fisher had been wrong – Mendel had not falsified his experiments.

Today the science of genetics – sired by Mendel, the celibate monk – influences our understanding of evolution, human development, physiology, biochemistry, medicine, agriculture and even social science. And British researchers recently described all the components that make up one of the genes responsible for the wrinkled pea pods that Mendel had studied so assiduously.

Below left: Darwin as ape – a contemporary cartoon.
Below: Photograph of Gregor Mendel. *Mary Evans*

MARIE CURIE
RADIOACTIVITY

Science Photo Library

THE LATE 19TH CENTURY – *when western Europe was more or less at peace – saw a burgeoning of experimental science and discovery. In the first five years of the 1890s, for instance, the electron was named, antitoxins were synthesised, argon was discovered, oxygen was liquefied, the first pieces of rayon were produced, the plague bacillus was isolated and the zip fastener was invented. And in the field of radiation, small advances were being made that would eventually have huge consequences.*

MAKING WAVES IN SCIENCE

In 1886, the 29-year-old German physicist Heinrich Hertz demonstrated the existence of radio waves, and smiled incredulously when it was predicted that, one day, these waves would be sent round the world. Only nine years after that, in 1895, Italian physicist Guglielmo Marconi sent the first radio signals. Six years later he transmitted them across the Atlantic.

A few months after Marconi's first experiment, in November 1895, Wilhelm Röntgen, a professor of physics at Würzburg University, accidentally discovered X-rays – the high-frequency counterpart to Hertz's waves. He later found that these rays – which he named 'X-rays' because their nature was unknown – could pass through everything but lead.

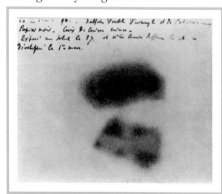

A few weeks after Röntgen's discovery, the French scientist Henri Becquerel set aside a Saturday to examine the X-ray potential of uranium salts, intending to place the substance on a photographic plate shielded by aluminium foil and then expose this to sunlight. However, the day was dull, so Becquerel placed the uranium and the shielded plate in a drawer. When he later developed the plate (*left*), he found that it had darkened at the spot where the uranium salts had been placed. So, he reasoned, the mineral must emit rays that, like X-rays, could penetrate matter. Becquerel published a number of papers on the subject but then lost interest.

1859
Pierre Curie born in Paris (15 May).

1867
Marya (Marie) Sklodowska born in Warsaw (7 November).

1878
Pierre begins work at the Sorbonne in Paris.

1891
Marie goes to study at the Sorbonne.

1894
Marie meets Pierre and graduates from the Sorbonne.

1895
Marie and Pierre marry.

1897
Marie gives birth to Irène and begins to work on uranium rays.

1898
The Curies announce the discovery of polonium (July) and radium (December).

1903
The Curies (and Henri Becquerel) are awarded the Nobel prize for physics, and Marie gives birth to Eve.

1906
Pierre dies after a road accident.

1910
Marie isolates pure radium.

1911
Marie is awarded the Nobel prize for chemistry, fails to be elected to the Académie des Sciences and endures a scandal over her relationship with Paul Langevin.

1934
Marie dies of leukaemia (4 July).

Two years later, in 1897, the 30-year-old Marie Curie chose the study of uranium rays for her doctoral thesis.

'MY PLANS FOR THE FUTURE? I HAVE NONE'

Marya Sklodowska was born on 7 November 1867 in Warsaw, at a time when Poland was under Russian domination. Soon after her birth, her parents lost their jobs as teachers and had to take in boarders. Despite working long hours helping with the lodgers' meals, Marya won a medal for excellence following examinations, held in Russian, at the local school.

However, there was no money to pay for Marya to go on to higher education. Instead, she took a job as a governess and sent most of her wages to her older sister, who was studying medicine in Paris. In 1891, after her sister had graduated, Marya joined her, and entered the Sorbonne. In a letter to her cousin before she left, she wrote: 'My plans for the future? I have none, or rather they are so commonplace ... that they are not worth talking about. I mean to get through as well as I can, and when I can do no more, say farewell to this base world. The loss will be small and regret for me will be short.' By 1894, Marya had graduated at the top of her class and earned masters degrees in both physics and mathematics.

In that year, Marie (as Marya was now known) met fellow scientist Pierre Curie. He was 35, eight years older than Marie, and already an outstanding physicist. He had chosen a life of solitude, writing: 'When we give our thoughts to work, we have to struggle against women ... women of genius are rare.' But despite his intentions, Pierre and Marie fell in love and in July 1895 were married at Sceaux, where his parents lived. Two years later, their daughter Irène was born, and within months, Marie was investigating uranium rays at the Sorbonne's School of Industrial Physics and Chemistry, where Pierre taught.

A MYSTERIOUS NEW ELEMENT

Marie's investigations led her to discover that, of all the elements then known, only uranium and thorium emitted rays. She also discovered that, in uranium compounds, the other elements seemed to have no effect on the amount of rays – known scientifically as 'radiation' – emitted; the important factor was the amount of uranium itself. From this, she hypothesised that the ability to produce radiation did not depend on the arrangement of atoms in a molecule but must be linked to some-thing happening in the interior of the uranium atom itself. This discovery was revolutionary and, to many scientists, is Marie Curie's most important contribution to physics.

During her study of uranium compounds, Marie had noticed that pitchblende – uranium oxide ore that occurs in tar-like masses – was at least four times as active as pure uranium. In April 1898, she wrote a short paper announcing the probable existence of a new element in pitchblende.

Pierre abandoned his own work on crystals and joined Marie in the race to discover the mysterious new element. Laboriously, they refined the small quantity of pitchblende available to them and, by the end of June 1898, had isolated a substance that was 330 times as active – or, as the Curies described it, 'radioactive' – as uranium. In July, they announced the discovery of the new element 'polonium', named after Marie's beloved Poland.

The refined pitchblende liquid left over from the polonium extraction was still very radioactive. The Curies believed that there had to be another undiscovered element in the ore. Further refining eventually produced a substance that was 900 times more radioactive than uranium. On 26 December 1898 the Curies announced the discovery of radium.

However, the next step was to produce pure radium. It was this work that has become legendary (*see box on page 20*).

'A CAUSE OF REAL SUFFERING'

Achievement brought fame, and Marie, in particular, became the focus of attention. The Curies were pursued by journalists from all over the world, and the experience nearly broke them. 'The shattering of our voluntary isolation was a cause of real suffering for us,' wrote Marie.

Both Marie and Becquerel had burned themselves accidentally while carrying phials of radium in their pockets and, in 1901, Pierre had burned himself

OPPOSITES ATTRACT

According to the historian Helena Pycior, who has studied the Curies' 'spousal collaboration', 'it was their complementarity that enabled them to do so much.' Pierre was a slow thinker who framed his scientific conclusions methodically and cared little for fame. Marie, on the other hand, moved quickly from experiments to bold hypotheses. Pierre's non-competitiveness probably held him back within the scientific establishment, but it also freed him to collaborate with his wife on equal terms. Intellectually restless, he jumped from one area of study to another, while Marie, although intellectually broad, was capable of immersing herself in one subject – radioactivity – for most of her life.

The fact that the Curies were outsiders – Marie a Pole and a woman, Pierre largely home-educated by a politically radical father – may have influenced their choice of scientific research. Most of the French scientific establishment was focusing on X-rays, while Marie and Pierre concentrated on the distinctly unfashionable uranium rays.

Above: A cartoon of Marie and Pierre Curie from a 1904 issue of *Vanity Fair* magazine.
Mary Evans

Facing page (top): The Sorbonne's School of Industrial Physics and Chemistry in 1884.
Mary Evans

TOILING IN THE POTATO CELLAR

Madame Curie.

Wyndham Ed.ⁿ Paris
W 104 ©

Above: A contemporary postcard of Marie Curie in her laboratory.
Mary Evans

Right: A sample of pitchblende: in 1898, Marie and Pierre Curie discovered radioactive radium and polonium in a similar sample. Today a 'curie' is a unit of radioactivity.
Astrid & Hanns-Frieder Michler/ Science Photo Library

RADIUM TURNED out to be only a one-millionth part of pitchblende. The Curies despaired when they realised that they needed a vast quantity of the expensive ore to recover any significant amount of the element.

However, they were able to buy cheaply eight tonnes of pitchblende slag (with the costly uranium already conveniently removed). This was deposited outside the abandoned shed, once a dissecting room, loaned to them as a workplace by the Sorbonne. The glass roof leaked, they roasted in summer and froze in winter; a visiting German chemist described their 'laboratory' as 'a cross between a stable and a potato cellar'.

For almost four years, the Curies worked in these primitive conditions. First, they ground up some of the pitchblende. Then they added an acid to it, which would react with some of the compounds in the ore, 'eat' them up and leave the rest. Then the ore/acid mixture was poured through a filter so that the solid material and the acid could be separated. Next, both components had to be tested to see which one contained the still-mysterious radioactive element. There were many acids to test and many useless elements in the ore, so this process had to be repeated thousands of times.

The work was physically difficult. Marie processed 20 kilograms (44lb) of raw material at a time. 'Sometimes I had to spend a whole day stirring a boiling mass with a heavy iron rod nearly as big as myself,' she wrote. 'I would be broken with fatigue at day's end.'

Pierre's teaching job could not support both a family and research, and in 1900, Marie was forced to take a part-time teaching post. Yet she wrote that these were 'the best and happiest years of our life'. The Curies' progress could be measured by sight: the refined liquid and crystals glowed in the dark. By 1902, they had isolated one-tenth of a gram of radium chloride. Marie announced their results in her doctoral thesis in June 1903.

Late in the year, the Curies shared the Nobel prize for physics with Henri Becquerel for their work on radioactivity. Their prize money - 70,000 francs – solved their financial worries, and the Sorbonne created a professorship for Pierre, with Marie as his chief assistant. Pregnant again, Marie celebrated the culmination of an extraordinary year with the birth of her daughter Eve.

deliberately by strapping some to his arm. The phenomenon excited him – X-rays were being used to treat cancer, so perhaps needles of radium would work as well. When, in 1904, it was proved that radium rays killed diseased cells preferentially, there was great commercial interest in the element. However, the Curies remained dedicated to science and refused to patent their refining process, thus failing to gain any financial benefit from their discoveries.

In 1906, tragedy struck when Pierre was killed by a horse-drawn cart in Paris. Marie was almost broken by grief, but her innate toughness came to the fore, and she accepted her fate as a widow and sole parent of two young daughters.

Refusing a state pension – 'I am 38 and able to support myself' – she was offered Pierre's post, so becoming the first woman professor at the Sorbonne. In 1911 she became the first person to be awarded a second Nobel prize – this time for chemistry – for her discovery and isolation (in 1910) of radium.

SCANDAL

However, 1911 was also Marie Curie's *annus horribilis*. When her name was put forward for election to the Académie des Sciences, she was greeted with xenophobia and misogyny. Her Polish origins were railed against, and in the end she lost the election by two votes.

But worse was to come. The newspapers began to speculate about her relationship with a married colleague Paul Langevin. Following a burglary at his flat, stolen letters allegedly written by Marie – 'When I know you are with her, my nights are atrocious, I can't sleep' – made their way into the press. Marie's house was besieged, while Langevin challenged a newspaper editor to a duel (in the end, no shots were fired).

The Nobel prize committee asked Marie not to come to Stockholm to receive her award until the scandal had died down. She wrote back saying that she could not accept that slander could affect the appreciation of scientific work. And in December 1911 she arrived in Stockholm to receive her prize.

THE LEGACY

Marie spent the rest of her life promoting radium and raising money to further work into radioactivity. She never equalled her early discoveries, but her work led to the new science of nuclear medicine. In this, the Curie connection continued. In January 1934, Marie's daughter Irène, also a scientist, and her husband Frédéric Joliot succeeded in inducing radioactivity in non-radioactive elements. The results – 'radio-isotopes' – would later be used extensively in medical diagnosis.

Marie and Pierre's work, along with that of Becquerel, also marked the beginning of nuclear physics, which eventually led to nuclear fission and the production of nuclear energy.

In 1935, Irène and Frédéric were awarded the Nobel prize for chemistry, but Marie was not there to share their triumph. In July 1934, at the age of 66, she died of pernicious anaemia, perhaps caused by leukaemia resulting from long exposure to radioactivity.

In April 1995, the ashes of Marie and Pierre were taken from the small cemetery at Sceaux and enshrined in the Panthéon in Paris. Thus Marie became the first woman to be honoured in her own right at the memorial to France's 'great men'.

Above: Marie and Pierre in 1904, the year after they won their joint Nobel prize. Pictured with them is their daughter Irène who would, with *her* husband, win a Nobel prize in 1935.
Science Museum/Science & Society Picture Library

Left: The Panthéon in Paris, the final resting place of Pierre and Marie Curie. *Mary Evans*

ALBERT EINSTEIN
THE THEORY OF RELATIVITY

AT THE END of 19th century, there was a feeling among scientists that they were close to comprehending how the eternal and unchanging universe worked. Newton's laws of mechanics described the nature of gravity and the interaction of bodies. Time and space were constants against which motion could be measured. The universe was like a wind-up clock – mechanical, predictable, understandable. Then a young German produced a theory that changed everything.

Albert Einstein was born to Jewish parents on 14 March 1879 in Ulm, Germany. With grim irony, his birth coincided with the foundation of the League of Anti-Semites. The world he entered was in turmoil. The Franco-Prussian war nine years earlier had led to the annexation of Alsace-Lorraine by the newly proclaimed German empire. The global financial crash of 1873 resulted in demographic and economic upheaval.

But it was also an era of enormous scientific innovation. Ørsted, Faraday, Maxwell, Hertz and others had discovered electromagnetism and proved that light itself was an electromagnetic wave. Radio waves had been discovered, too – Marconi was developing the first radios when Einstein was a boy. Through an understanding of the laws of thermodynamics, which explain the behaviour of gases under the influence of pressure and temperature, steam engines came into being.

In short, as the 20th century approached, science appeared to offer unprecedented knowledge and mastery of the world. During Einstein's youth, Germany was in the process of massive industrialisation, driven by the chemical and electrical industries. Science was being put to practical use like never before. The electrification of the railways was just beginning. Electric street lighting had taken over from gas lamps. Manufacturing had been revolutionised, creating wealth and transforming lives.

THE CONSEQUENCES OF A COMPASS

Albert's father Hermann Einstein, an electrical engineer, had set up in business with his brother Jacob, manufacturing dynamos and electrical instruments. But after initial success, they were hit hard by the crash of '73 and were eventually crushed by the newly emerging electro-chemical conglomerates. The Einstein business at Ulm finally failed in 1880 and the family moved to Munich.

Albert's early years showed none of the promise he was later to fulfil. He was slow to talk, contemplative and a little introverted. He found it difficult to fit in at school, perhaps because he was the only Jewish child in a Catholic institution, although his parents were not religious. He did not warm to the militaristic regimes of any of the schools he attended, with their emphasis on discipline, learning by rote and vigorous exercise, but preferred playing at home with his sister Maja, two years his junior.

It was within the family, free from the rigid confines of the authoritarian schools, that Albert embraced academic studies and began to display his father's flair for mathematics and, under his mother's tutelage, a fondness for music. He showed a quiet determination and patience, whether solving puzzles or building houses of cards.

Right: Guglielmo Marconi and some of his inventions. *Mary Evans*

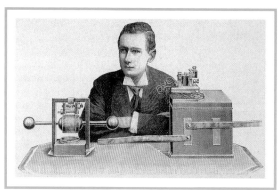

1879
Born at Ulm, Germany (14 March).

1884
Compass from his father awakes interest in science.

1896
Starts course in maths and physics teaching at Eidgenössoche Technische Hochschule (ETH), Zurich, Switzerland.

1901
Begins work at Swiss Patent Office in Berne. Takes Swiss citizenship.

1903
Marries Mileva Maric.

1905
Einstein's annus mirabilis: publishes his Special Theory of Relativity - E=mc² - and two other revolutionary scientific papers.

1912
Appointed to professorship at ETH in Zurich.

1914
Accepts directorship of Institute of Physics at the Kaiser Wilhelm Institute, Berlin.

Albert's interest in science was whetted at the age of five when his father gave him a compass to play with. The little boy was fascinated by this unseen force of magnetism, which, mysteriously and magically, always made the needle point in the same direction. His uncle Jacob introduced him to algebra and a family friend got him interested in geometry and calculus. He read and read, developing an interest in philosophy as well as science and maths.

Popular science books shook his belief in the literal truths of the Bible, and this fuelled a distrust of the authoritarian and militaristic institutions that dominated German culture at the time. At a relatively early age, Albert developed a strong scepticism about accepted beliefs in any sphere – a trait that was to help him confound the scientific establishment in later years.

When the Einsteins moved to the Italian city of Milan in 1894, after yet another business failure, Albert stayed behind to complete his schooling. He had a terrible time and eventually left, having persuaded a doctor to give him a certificate saying he was suffering from a nervous breakdown. He joined his family in Italy, thereby escaping the military service then compulsory in Germany.

In Italy, Hermann Einstein's business failed twice more and the family faced financial ruin. Albert had no diploma and couldn't enter university without one. At his first attempt, he failed the entrance exam for the Eidgenössoche Technische Hochschule (ETH), an excellent polytechnic in Zurich. He went instead to Aarau, a small Swiss school where he flourished in the more relaxed regime. His graduation from there in 1896 at the age of 17 coincided with the renunciation of his German citizenship. He felt happy to be free of a country whose militaristic institutions and anti-Semitism he detested. He now retook the ETH exam, this time passing it, and began a course specialising in the teaching of physics and mathematics.

THE ARROGANT STUDENT

During his time at ETH (1896-1900), Einstein was particularly interested in the generally accepted theory that light and electromagnetic radiation had to pass through something. As sound needs air or another medium to create its waves, so light must require a similar kind of substance, which was called the 'ether' for want of a better word. However, nobody knew what the ether was or had managed to measure it. Einstein's attempt to do so in the ETH laboratory resulted in an injured hand and the disapprobation of his superiors.

He realised that, under the current Newtonian theory, if he travelled at the speed of light and held a mirror in front of himself, he wouldn't be able to see his reflection – because, relative to him, light would be stationary. That didn't seem to make sense. He would later return to this problem.

In many ways, Einstein was a typical student – shabbily dressed, attending only the few lectures that interested him and keen on women (he met his first wife, Mileva Maric, at the polytechnic). But he was also extremely self-assured, even arrogant – this was a man who had had the chutzpah to reject his own country as a teenager. He did not like being told what to do, and got into trouble with the head of ETH, Heinrich Weber, for questioning accepted theories. Einstein believed freedom of thought was the key to scientific progress and disliked any attempt at forced learning.

It was this combination of natural intelligence, independence and fierce determination that enabled Einstein to challenge the accepted Newtonian view of physics and eventually turn the world of science on its head.

After graduating from ETH, he did the odd teaching job, but was blocked from any major academic post by Weber. This only spurred Einstein on: in 1901, he became a Swiss citizen and took up a post in the Swiss Patent Office in Berne; and two years later, he married Mileva.

The nature of light and its movement continued to fascinate Einstein, but his early scientific papers concerned the forces between molecules and the laws of thermodynamics. Yet they contained flaws and failed to win him recognition. It wasn't until 1905 – at the age of only 26 – that he made his mark with three papers, the most famous of which was his Special Theory of Relativity. Ten years later, building on this work, he produced his General Theory of Relativity – which changed our understanding of the universe for ever (*see box on page 24*).

Albert Einstein in 1922. *Mary Evans*

1915
Publishes the General Theory of Relativity – gravity can make space bend.

1919
Eddington proves Einstein's theory by measuring positions of stars during an eclipse. Einstein divorces Mileva Maric, marries cousin Elsa Löwenthal.

1921
Wins Nobel Prize for Physics for work on quantum physics.

1930s onwards
Searches for unifying theory of physics.

1932
Moves to the US.

1933
Takes permanent job at Princeton University, New Jersey.

1940
Takes American citizenship.

1955
Dies at Princeton (18 April).

THE BREAKTHROUGH

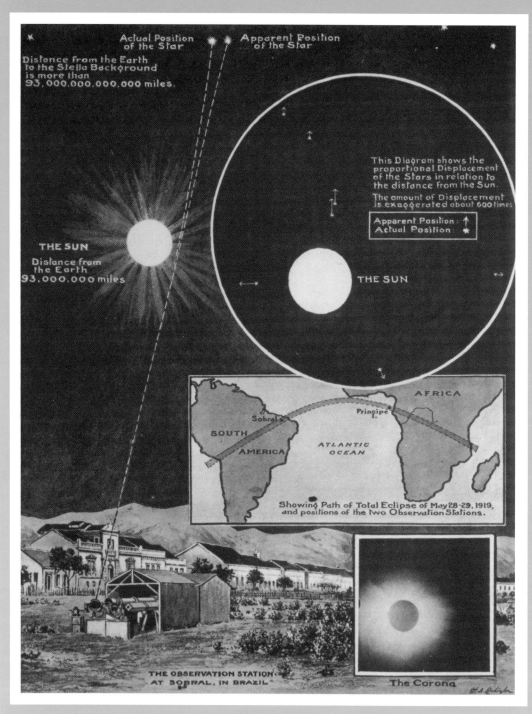

Diagram from a 22 November 1919 issue of the *Illustrated London News*, explaining the experiment carried out by Arthur Eddington that finally proved Einstein correct.

light, even if you kept applying force (energy) to it. Instead of constantly increasing the velocity, the energy being applied would increase the mass of the object to the point of infinity. This conclusion is encapsulated in the famous equation $E=mc^2$, with 'E' standing for energy, 'm' for mass and 'c' for the speed of light.

The paper made Einstein's reputation in academic circles and led to a professorship, first in Prague in 1911 and then in Zurich in 1912. Three years later, in 1915, he published his General Theory of Relativity, which incorporated the force of gravity into the Special Theory.

In the General Theory, Einstein came up with something even more extraordinary than $E=mc^2$. He argued that acceleration and gravity were the same – the principle of equivalence. If a space rocket was accelerating at close to the speed of light, and a beam of light was shone through a window on to the rocket's inner wall, the beam would appear to bend. But light can only move in straight lines and has no mass, so how can it be subject to the force of gravity? Einstein predicted that gravity/ acceleration must make space bend. Therefore, the gravitational pull exerted by the planets and stars must be accompanied by a perceived bending of light as it passes the planets and stars.

Einstein's theory predicted exactly how much the light – or rather, the space through which it travelled – would bend. All he needed to do now was test this by measuring the position of stars near the Sun during a solar eclipse and then comparing these measurements with the stars' positions six months earlier. There should be a discrepancy owing to the bending of the light from the stars as it passed the Sun.

But World War I intervened and delayed him. In the end, it was down to British astronomer Arthur Eddington to prove the theory. In 1919, he organised two expeditions – one to Sobral in Brazil and the other to Principe, an island off the west coast of Africa – at a time when a solar eclipse was scheduled to take place. Photographs of the stars were taken at each location during the eclipse and their exact positions were measured. Eddington then superimposed these photographs on to ones taken six months earlier. Although the deflection of the stars' light was tiny – the width of a human hair seen from about 14m (45ft) away – it exactly matched Einstein's prediction. The theory had been proved.

THE SPEED OF LIGHT – 300,000 kilometres (186,000 miles) per second – is a constant. But speed is distance divided by time, so if a moving observer and a stationary observer measure the same speed for light, it follows that the other parts of the equation – distance and time – must vary, or be relative, according to the observer. This was the core of Einstein's Special Theory of Relativity.

The conclusions of this theory are startling: a clock travelling fast will run more slowly than a stationary one (that is, time itself could slow down or speed up) and the lengths of moving objects will contract. This radical theory also predicted that nothing could go faster than

THE WRITING ON THE WALL

When Eddington released his data at a joint meeting of the Royal Society and the Royal Astronomical Society in London on 6 November 1919, Einstein was hailed as a hero by the scientists. After 200 years, Newton's law of gravity had been found to be incomplete. The accepted model of the way the universe worked had been permanently and fundamentally changed.

A war-weary world leapt upon the discovery – it made newspaper headlines everywhere. Like Marie Curie before him, Einstein found himself an instant celebrity, constantly harangued by journalists. His theories were not understood by many, but they still captured the public imagination. They even influenced the architectural principles of his friend, Erich Mendelsohn, who incorporated them in the sculptural Einstein Tower at Potsdam, which he designed immediately after the General Theory was proved. Within a year, more than 100 books had been published about the subject. Einstein had become a superstar – a cigar was even named after him and his 'absent-minded professor' image came to be known across the globe. But the object of all this celebrity had lost his much-prized freedom.

It is a great irony that Einstein finally won fame in the country that he had despised and rejected – in 1914, he had been appointed director of the Institute of Physics at the Kaiser Wilhelm Institute in Berlin. But he paid a heavy price: in 1919, his marriage to Mileva was dissolved. The souring of their relationship also affected his relationship with his two sons, a cause of great regret to him for many years to come. But he found consolation in a second marriage, to his cousin Elsa Löwenthal.

The rise of anti-Semitism in Germany saw Einstein once more exiled from his homeland. His heightened profile had led to lecture tours around the world, and while he was at the California Institute of Technology (1932–3), Hitler came to power. Einstein saw the writing on the wall and decided to stay in the United States, where he lived for the rest of his life, taking American citizenship in 1940.

Einstein is widely believed to have invented the atomic bomb. This isn't true, although his work did form the basis for its invention. However, even this most committed of pacifists advocated its development during World War II for fear that the Nazis would get there first. But he hated his association with the bomb and, after the war, became actively involved in the movement to abolish nuclear weapons.

Einstein's discoveries in the field of quantum physics resulted in the invention of lasers – every CD player owes its existence to him. His later work led to theories about the existence of five or more dimensions, the successful identification of black holes and the Big Bang theory. However, like Faraday, he was unsuccessful in finding the one unified theory of forces – gravity stubbornly continues to evade inclusion. But, despite not achieving this final goal, Einstein unlocked the doors to the universe for generations of scientists who followed him.

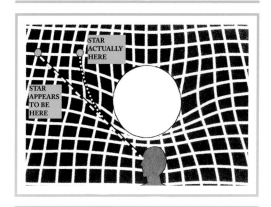

Above: How, according to Einstein, the gravitational pull of a celestial body can bend space and so make stars appear to be where they should not be.

Below left: Einstein's fame lives on: in Nicolas Roeg's 1985 film *Insignificance*, Einstein (Michael Emil) discusses his theory of relativity with Marilyn Monroe (Theresa Russell). *BFI Films*

RESOURCES

GALILEO GALILEI

Books

Galileo and the Solar System by Paul Strathern (Arrow, 1998) £3.99.
One of a series giving clear accounts of major discoveries.

Galileo's Daughter by Dava Sobel (Fourth Estate, 1999) £16.99.
A new perspective on the life of Galileo through the correspondence of his daughter, the nun Sister Marie Celeste.

Galileo in 90 Minutes by John and Mary Gribbin (Constable, 1997) £3.50.
A potted history of Galileo from the leading 'husband and wife' physics popularisers.

The Cambridge Companion to Galileo by Peter Machamer (Cambridge University Press, 1998) £14.95.
A collection of essays that takes a serious look at the life and times of Galileo.

Websites

Inclined planes and frictional forces
http://zebu.uoregon.edu/nsf/friction.html
Part of an online educational package from the University of Oregon. Includes various options to try out virtual versions of the inclined plane experiment and many others.

Institute and Museum of History of Science, Florence
http://galileo.imss.firenze.it/vr/eavv.html
A virtual tour of the museum in the heart of Galileo country.

Galileo Galilei
www-groups.dcs.st-and.ac.uk/~history/Mathematicians/Galileo.html
A detailed biography with lots of links and a section of quotations showing the wit and wisdom of the 'wrangler'.

The Galileo Project
http://es.rice.edu/ES/humsoc/Galileo/
Rice University in Texas provides the low-down on Galileo with descriptions of his experiments, a biography and a detailed chronology.

SIR ISAAC NEWTON

Books

Isaac Newton: The last sorcerer by Michael White (Fourth Estate, 1998) £8.99.
In-depth review of Newton's life by the well-known science writer, looking particularly at Newton's fascinating obsession with alchemy.

Newton for Beginners by William Rankin (Icon Books, 1993) £8.99.
Fun, pictorial approach to the subject – gives a good overview of the main points in Newton's life.

On Giants' Shoulders by Melvyn Bragg (Sceptre, 1998) £7.99.
A series of essays based on the Radio 4 series, with Newton just one of many influential innovators in the history of science. An accessible introduction that also helps put Newton in context.

The Colour of Light – The story of Isaac Newton by Meredith Hooper (Wayland Publishers, 1997) £4.50.
A children's (and adult-accessible) introduction to Newton's light experiments.

Websites

Newtonia
www.newtonia.freeserve.co.uk
Comprehensive collection of links to other Newton sites, containing biographies, academic studies and related materials. Very good starting point.

Isaac Newton Institute for Mathematical Sciences
www.newton.cam.ac.uk
Excellent, academic site from this institution in Cambridge. It has a 'Newton Resources' section that gives you plenty of links to other Newton-related websites.

St Andrew's University
www-groups.dcs.st-and.ac.uk/~history/Mathematicians/Newton.html
Thoroughly researched site, giving biographies and lots of other resources.

University of Kentucky
http://csep10.phys.utk.edu/astr161/lect/history/newton.html
A section on Newton taken from the university's astronomy course, explaining his theories and providing biographical links.

MICHAEL FARADAY
Books
Atoms, Electrons and Change by P W Atkins (Scientific American Library, New York, 1991). A modern spin on Faraday's 'Candle' lecture. Out of print but possibly available from libraries.

The Chemical History of a Candle by Michael Faraday and Jeanyee Wong (Cherokee, 1978) £12.95. The archetypal popularisation of a science lecture.

The Forces of Matter by Michael Faraday (Prometheus Books, 1993) £7.50. From the horse's mouth.

Michael Faraday and the Royal Institution by John Meurig Thomas and Brian Pippard (Adam Hilger Ltd, 1991) £16.95. Leading scientists recount the tale of one of the Royal Institution's biggest names.

Spiritual Science, Electricity and Michael Faraday by Ernst Lehrs (Rudolf Steiner Press, 1975) £2.00.

Websites
Michael Faraday (1791–1867)
www.iee.org.uk/publish/faraday/faraday1.html
The Institution of Electrical Engineers' site on one of their great forebears.

Michael Faraday (1791–1867)
www.ri.ac.uk/History/M.Faraday
The Royal Institution's site provides a reasonably definitive history.

GREGOR MENDEL
Books
Experiments in Plant Hybridization by Gregor Mendel (Harvard University Press, 1965) £6.50. Relatively recent edition of the original work.

Gregor Mendel and the Roots of Genetics by Edward Edelson (Oxford University Press, 1999) £13. Update on Mendelism for young adults.

Mendel in 90 Minutes by John and Mary Gribbin (Constable, 1997) £3.50. A brief history of Mendel in 'popular' style.

Websites
Gregor Mendel
www.mvhs.srvusd.k12.ca.us/~aallman/mendel.html
Part of the Fundamentals of Genetics site originally aimed at US high school students.

Gregor Mendel's Legacy
http://bioserve.latrobe.edu.au/vcebiol/cat3/u4aos1p4.html
Australian university's spin on Mendel's laws and history, genotypes, di-hybrids and dominance.

MendelWeb
www.netspace.org/MendelWeb/
An educational resource about classical genetics, data analysis, plant science and the history and literature of science.

MARIE CURIE
Books
Curie in 90 Minutes by John and Mary Gribbin (Constable, 1997) £3.50. Concise, 80-page account of Marie Curie's life and achievements, by two renowned science writers.

Madame Curie: A biography by Eve Curie (translated by Vincent Sheean) (Da Capo Press, 1986) £13.50. Marie Curie's life by her daughter, first published in 1938.

Marie Curie: A life by Susan Quinn (Mandarin, 1996) £7.99. Not only describes Marie Curie's research, but also explores her early life in Russia-dominated Poland, her affair with Paul Langevin, and her passion for Pierre.

The Big Idea: Curie and radioactivity by Paul Strathern (Arrow, 1998) £3.99. This gives a clear, accessible explanation of the meaning and importance of the discovery of radioactivity and the implications this has had for society.

Websites
Marie Curie
http://nobelprizes.com/nobel/physics/1903c.html
Links from the Nobel Prize Internet Archive.

Marie and Pierre Curie and the Discovery of Polonium and Radium
www.nobel.se/essays/curie/index.html
The text of an informative lecture by Nanny Fröman at the Royal Academy of Sciences in Stockholm in 1996, on the Nobel Foundation website.

ALBERT EINSTEIN

Books

Einstein: A life in Science by Michael White and John Gribbin (Pocket Books, 1994) £6.99.
Excellent detailed biography by two well-respected scientific authors. It clearly explains the theories without introducing unintelligible mathematics.

Introducing Einstein by Joseph Schwartz and Michael McGuinness (Icon Books, 1999) £8.99.
A witty, pictorial approach to the subject, giving readers just enough information to get to grips with the basics of Einstein's theories.

The Big Idea: Einstein and relativity by Paul Strathern (Arrow, 1997) £3.99.
Very simple introduction to Einstein, giving you enough to get you through dinner parties without embarrassment.

The Quotable Einstein, collected and edited by Alice Calaprice (Princeton University Press, 1996) £13.75.
Useful anthology of Einstein's sayings and speeches for an understanding of the man behind the theories.

Websites

Albert Einstein: German/American physicist
www2.lucidcafe.com/lucidcafe/library/96mar/einstein.html
Brief snapshot of Einstein's life, with reviews of books and links to other resources. On the Lucid Café website.

Albert Einstein Institute
www.aei-potsdam.mpg.de/about/index.html
Academic institute studying gravitational forces. Excellent resource for the serious Einstein student, with academic research papers and links to other websites.

Albert Einstein Online
www.westegg.com/einstein
Very comprehensive set of links to Einstein-related web pages, including biographies, related theories of physics, Einstein's own writings, pictures and other writings. Just about everything you might want to know.

Einstein Revealed
www.pbs.org/wgbh/nova/einstein
Fun educational resource for students and teachers. Not too academic and nicely, presented with good graphics and animations. On the Nova Online website.